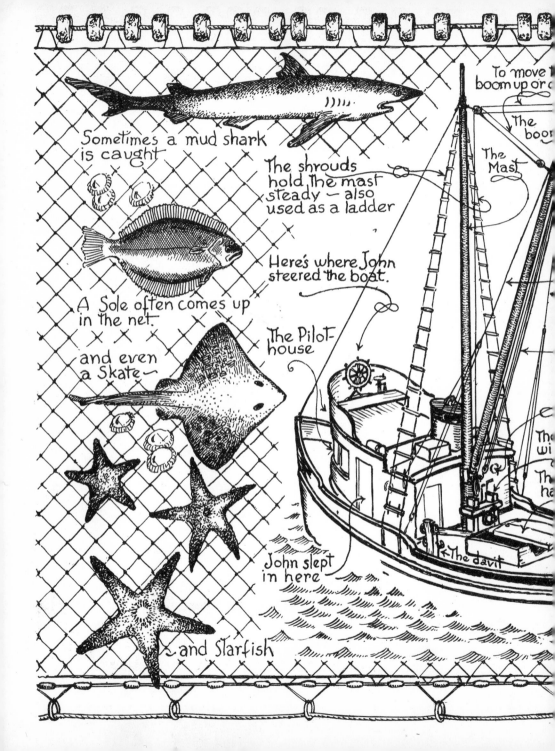

Sometimes a mud shark is caught

The shrouds hold the mast steady — also used as a ladder

A Sole often comes up in the net.

Here's where John steered the boat.

and even a Skate —

The Pilot-house

John slept in here

and Starfish

To move the boom up or down

The boom

The Mast

The davit

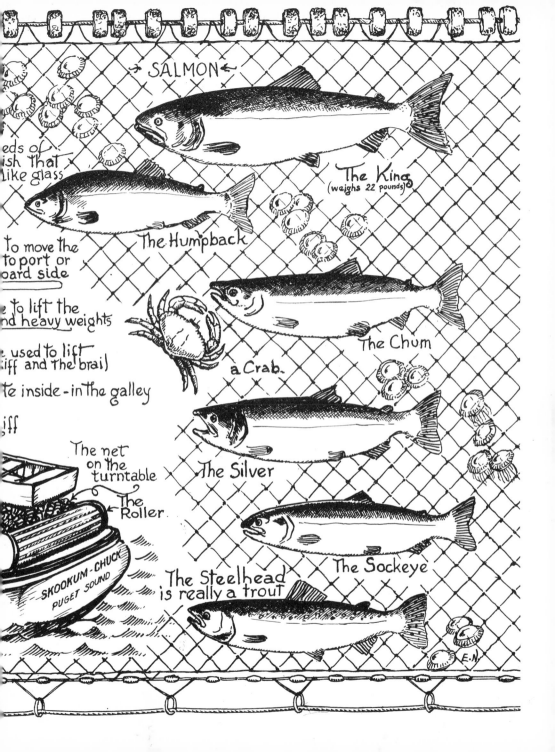

SALMON

The King
(weighs 22 pounds)

The Humpback

eds of
ish that
like glass

to move the
to port or
oard side

e to lift the
nd heavy weights

e used to lift
iff and the brail

te inside - in the galley

iff

a Crab.

The Chum

The net
on the
turntable

The
Roller.

The Silver

SKOOKUM-CHUCK
PUGET SOUND

The Steelhead
is really a trout

The Sockeye

E.N.

POGO'S FISHING TRIP

A Story of Salmon

POGO'S FISHING TRIP
A Story of Salmon

Jo and Ernest Norling

Holt, Rinehart and Winston
New York • Chicago • San Francisco

POGO'S FISHING TRIP

A Story of Salmon

Mother and John and Daddy were going to visit Uncle
Edward. Mother packed two big suitcases and John
packed two little ones. Pogo, John's dog, packed
nothing at all but he stayed very near the car and watched
carefully. He wanted to be sure to go along.

I

"Hurry, John!" called Father. He was putting the big suitcase in the car.

"Wait!" said John, "I have to get something!" Soon he came running, a small suitcase in each hand and something else tucked under his arm.

"What is that you have?" asked Mother.

"A fish bowl!" answered John.

"Fish bowl! Why are you taking that?" asked Mother.

"Well, you see," explained John, "a fish bowl is a house for a fish and this house needs a fish to live in it. Uncle Edward told me when he was here that he catches lots of fish. So when I go fishing with him I'll just pick one out and plop it right in here."

"Why, of course!" said Father smiling at Mother.

"Of course!" smiled Mother. "Get in the car and we'll be on our way."

John and Pogo sat in the front seat of the car with Father. Sometimes John played he was driving the car and sometimes he just looked out the windows at the hills and trees. They rode a long time and then John said, "Look, Pogo! There's the ocean!"

"It is just a small part of the big ocean beyond," said Father. "It is called Puget Sound. And look! There's our ferry boat – just coming in."

"The road goes down over the water to meet it," said John.

"Yes, that's the dock. The big boats have to stay in deep water." Father stopped behind the last car in line. They were all waiting.

Then the boat's whistle called "Toot!"

"They are ready to load," said Father.

A man waved his hand and said "Go head!" All the cars in line drove right inside the ferry. They had to get close together so there would be room for all of them.

"This looks like a parking lot," said John.

"That's just what it is," laughed Father. "Shall we go up on the very top deck?"

"Oh yes!" John jumped from the car. "Come on, Pogo!"

From the top deck they could see all around. John had never seen so much water. "What a lot of fish must live there!" he said.

He watched the ducks ride on the waves like little boats.

"Look at them, Pogo! I wish I could ride like that, just me, without anything to stand on."

But Pogo wouldn't look. "Woof!" He kept watching the big seagulls flying over him. They seemed to stay still in the air above him and then suddenly fly down right over his nose. "Woof!"

Mother gave John a box of crackers. John counted out the crackers until they were all gone. "One for me, one for you, Pogo, and one for the seagulls." Pogo ate his crackers from the deck but the seagulls picked theirs from the water where John threw them.

"Well," said Mother, "we will soon be there. Look! You can see Uncle Edward's house just above the beach near all those fishing boats. Uncle Edward will be watching for us."

"Come," said Father, "we must get in the car and be ready to drive off the ferry when it gets to the dock."

"Mother and I will drive in the car," said Father. "John, you and Pogo may go that way down those steps to the beach. There's Uncle Edward waiting for you."

What a lot of fun it was running with Pogo on the wet sand!

"Hi there!" called Uncle Edward, "it's about time you came to see me." He gave John a big hug. "Is this your pup?"

"Yes, that's Pogo. He is grown up now. Do you catch lots of fish?"

"Lots of fish? Well now, I'll show you when we go out on the boat. I guess your dad will let you go along tomorrow."

"Oh yes, he said I could."

"Woof!" barked Pogo.

Uncle Edward laughed. "All right, you can go too." He patted Pogo on the head. "Yes sir, you can both go. I think we need a couple more hands to help us set the net."

He threw a stick into the water for Pogo to bring back. "Say, that dog is a good swimmer, isn't he?" Pogo dropped the stick at Uncle Edward's feet. "Woof!" he answered.

8

After dinner John took off his shoes and stockings and waded in the cold water. He liked to dig his toes in the sand under the water and feel the little crabs crawl over his feet. And all the while, he watched the men get his uncle's boat ready to take out fishing. Her name was the *Alice B.,* and the men looked her over carefully, oiled the engine and scrubbed the deck.

John could see the net piled high on the turntable, folded back and forth as he folded paper into little fans.

"That's so it will come off the boat fast when they want it in the water, Uncle Edward says," he told Pogo. But Pogo didn't care about nets for he was playing with a crab.

"Oh boy!" sang John. "I bet we're going to have hotcakes and honey." The men were putting boxes and cans of food on the boat.

Mother called from the house. "Uncle Edward says you had better get your things and go to bed on the boat tonight. They are going to leave before the sun is up in the morning."

"Whee!" John was soon ready to go.

John and Pogo hurried down a long narrow board walk that floated on the water and led to the *Alice B.*

"All aboard!" shouted Uncle Edward. "Step right up on these boxes and on to the deck. John, I want you to meet Bill and Ole, two of the best fishermen that ever lived. Maybe they'll tell you some of their fish stories about the ones that didn't get away."

"Sure will! I've got some good stories I've been saving just for you," said Ole, "but what's that big dish you have under your arm? Looks like you want a lot of mush for breakfast."

"No," said John, "that's a fish bowl."

"A fish bowl?" asked Bill. "What for?"

"For a fish, of course!" said Uncle. "He wants to get one when we bring in the nets."

"Oh yes, I see!" laughed Bill.

"Sonny, you can take your pick of the whole catch," promised Ole. "It's a gift from me."

"'Early to bed and early to rise!' Come into the cabin and I'll show you your bunks." Uncle Edward led the way. "One for you and one for Pogo." But Pogo didn't want a bunk to himself. He climbed on to the foot of John's bunk and they both went fast asleep.

When John awakened, he was rocking gently back and forth and he could hear the *chug chug* of the boat's engine. The morning's first light was just coming through a round window.

"Oh, the boat is going!" John jumped quickly from bed and looked out the port hole. The *Alice B.* was already far from shore. He could see other fishing boats, some near them and some way across the water.

John was all dressed in two minutes. He shivered, because it was cold on the boat in the early morning before the sun was up.

"Come along, Pogo, you sleepyhead! I smell breakfast." He ran into the galley.

"Woof!" Pogo jumped from the bunk and soon was with John.

"Good morning, fisherman!" called Bill. "You had better hurry. Here, get this stack of hotcakes on your plate before Ole eats them all."

"Me?" asked Ole. "Say, I've only had ten so far. I don't eat so much. How about me having three or four fried eggs, Shorty?" he asked the cook.

"Coming up," said Shorty. "Here's one first for John. Anything else you want, young fellow?"

John looked at his full plate. "Only some honey, please."

Uncle Edward added, "And just to keep him healthy, a cup of that milk we brought along for him. When you have finished eating, John, come out and help me at the wheel. I'll show you how to steer a boat."

"Are we fishing now?" asked John.

"Not yet. First we must go to where the fish are running." Uncle Edward put on his coat.

"Running? You mean swimming fast?" asked John.

Uncle laughed. "I'll tell you about it when you come out. I have to go now so that Jim, who is steering the boat, can come in to breakfast."

16

John hurried through his breakfast and soon he was out on deck with Uncle Edward. Steering the *Alice B.* was fun! Sometimes they passed between islands and points of land. Then all the boats looked as though they were in a parade for they kept right in the middle of the channel where the water was deepest. As they moved along, Uncle Edward told John about the fishing.

"The salmon," he said, "grow from eggs laid in the little rivers. There they live until they are big enough to swim down to the ocean. They live in the ocean until they are three or four years old. Then they go back to the rivers they came from to lay their eggs. To get there, they travel many miles, – thousands and thousands of salmon together. When that happens, each year, we say, 'The salmon are running!' When we find a place where they are running, we can catch many of them at one time."

"How do you catch them?" asked John.

"We purse-seine. 'Seine' is another name for net and 'purse' means we pull it together with strings." Uncle Edward took a pencil and a piece of paper from his pocket. "You can't see the net when it is under the water so I'll draw you some pictures. When we get to fishing, you will know what is happening."

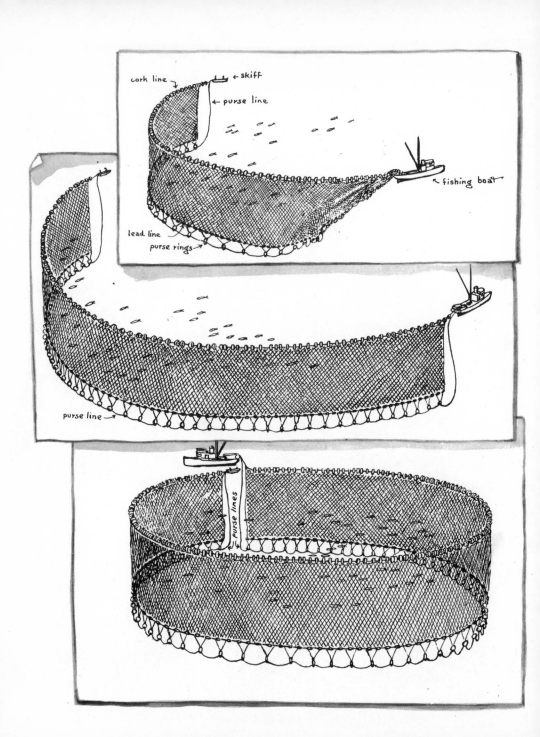

cork line

skiff

purse line

fishing boat

lead line

purse rings

purse line

purse lines

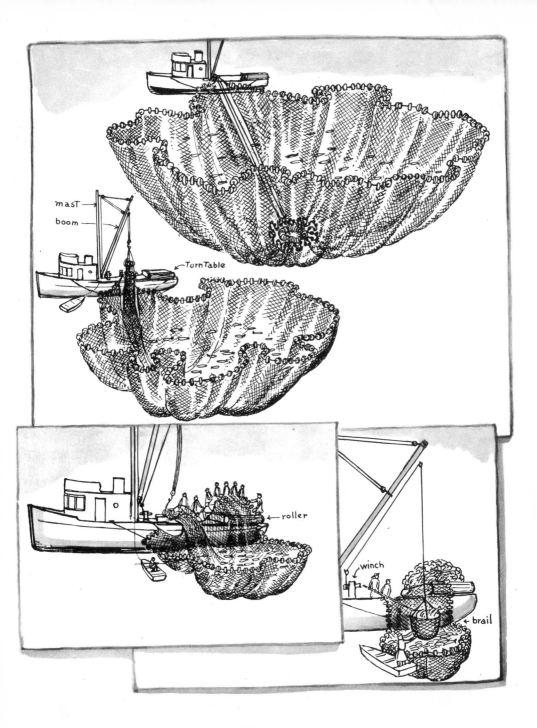

mast

boom

TurnTable

roller

winch

brail

After a while the boat slowed down. "Is this where the fish are running?" John asked.

"Yes," said Uncle Edward. "At least, we hope so."

Ole and Bill were loading things into the rowboat. "How about helping us set the net?" Ole called. "Want to be along with us in the skiff, John?"

"Oh yes! And Pogo too?"

"Woof!" said Pogo.

The skiff was lowered to the water and they all climbed down into it. One of the men tossed Bill two lines from the end of the net. Bill caught them and fastened them to the skiff. "The cork line and the purse line," he said. "Do you know which is the cork line?"

"Yes," said John. "The cork line floats on the water."

"Right! – Haul away!" Bill called. The *Alice B.* went away as fast as she could go. As she moved away, the net unfolded and dropped into the water. John could see the corks bobbing up and down on the waves.

"The rest of the net is held down under the water by the heavy lead weights. This makes the net like a high fence," explained Ole. "It stops the salmon that are in front and the rest just keep on coming in. Now you see the net is all off the boat. The boat goes slowly now, coming around in a big circle to where we are. Now we

have both ends of the net together. The fence is around the fish."

"Can't the fish jump over?" asked John.

"They can but they won't. They would rather stay under the water."

"Then why don't they swim out under the net?" John asked.

"Well, they don't usually swim that deep, and before they make up their minds to try it, we'll have the bottom of the net pulled together. But here's an open place where they can get out so I have to do this to keep them back." Ole kept a long stick moving up and down in the water between the two ends of the net. "If you look down into the water here, you can see some of them turn back. They don't want to pass me so they will try some other direction."

Bill untied the cork line and the purse line and handed them up to the man waiting to take them.

"Up with you!" He lifted John and Pogo into the *Alice B.* again, and then climbed aboard. "You watch right close now and you'll see how we purse the net. We slip this big wooden davit into a notch here and brace it with this long bar."

"The cork lines fasten on these hooks here." Bill tied them on. "These snatch blocks open so we can put the purse lines through; — then we wrap the ends around these spools on the winch . . . all set!" he called.

The boat's engine began to turn the spool and the lines were wrapped around and around it the way John wrapped the string on his top. John couldn't see what was happening under the water. He was glad Uncle Edward had made him some pictures.

"They are pulling the net together," he said. "They are pursing it."

The boat's engines kept winding the lines until Bill called, "Hold her! Here comes the lead!"

John looked over the side of the boat. "All of the rings are together now."

"All ready for this." Bill slipped a heavy rope through the rings and fastened the ends to a big iron hook that hung on a rope from the boom. The boat's engine pulled on the ropes and the net was lifted high above the deck. The rings came first, then the leads, and then the net all dripping with water.

The sun sparkled on bits of wet sea plants and on thousands of little round bright things caught in the net.

"What are those?" asked John.

"Jellyfish. They look like little umbrellas when they are swimming in the water," called Bill. "Sometimes the lower edge of the net drags along the bottom and picks things up. It pulls a few starfish off the rocks. See! There's a purple one in the net."

"Oh yes! I see three. They have points like a star. And there's one that's orange color like a star, too. Why aren't there any fish?"

"They keep swimming. They are still down there in the water. We had better find another place for you. You are standing on the hatch. That's where we put the fish down into the boat. We might kind of get you mixed up with the fish, and I don't think your daddy would like that." Bill swung John up on top of the cabin. "There's the right place for you." He gave the signal and the pursed end of the net was lowered to the deck. "This part of the boat is going to be plenty busy for awhile."

And it was busy! All of the men worked. The big table was turned so that the long roller was at the side of the boat. Then the men started pulling in the end of the net over the roller. The roller turned and helped them.

As the net came up, two of the men straightened out the purse line and spread the rings out along it. They were careful not to break any strings in the net and to stack it just right so that it would be ready to set again for the next time.

More and more of the net came on board while in the water the circle of cork floats became smaller and smaller. Ole stayed in the skiff to see that they did not get tangled. He watched, too, so that he could tell the men when they had pulled in enough net. If they pulled in too much, the fish would be spilled back into the water.

"Hold her!" he shouted. The men stopped pulling and the roller stopped turning. "Get the brail!"

The hook was swung out over the fish. A bowl-shaped net with a long handle was hung on to the big hook.

John climbed down to the deck again. "Do you fish with that, too?" he asked.

Uncle laughed. "Well, you see there are a lot of fish down there — tons of them. This is a big catch. If we tried to bring them all up at once in the large net, they might be so heavy they'd break right through."

The brail was lowered into the water and came up full of wiggling fish. A man held the long handle to keep it from spilling until it was over the deck.

"Stand back! Here they spill!" Uncle Edward pulled John out of the way just in time. Out came the fish, jumping and turning so John could see the light silver color of the underside of their bodies.

"Whee!" said John. "What big fish! Some are almost as large as I am. They can jump higher than I can, too! Look out, Pogo!"

The brail dipped again and again over the side of the boat. John and Pogo would watch until it was over the deck. Then, when the brail was ready to spill, they would run as fast as they could out of the way.

Some of the fishermen kept pulling in the net while others pushed the salmon down the hatch.

"We want only the salmon." Uncle Edward pushed the other fish to one side of the deck where John could look at them. There were many strange looking fish. "Even the salmon are not all just alike. There are different kinds."

"Do you go home when the boat is full?" asked John.

"No, the buyers come along with their boats and take them ashore for us. We can stay here for a few days and keep right on setting our net as long as the salmon are running, or we can move over to a new place where they are running. Here comes the last brail. Now we can pull in the rest of the net."

"Wait!" John turned to run away. "Wait!" he called again, "I have to get something."

But the men did not wait. They kept the net moving up.

"O. K." called Ole. "Here she comes!" He helped hold up the last of the net and threw it up onto the boat. There were only a few fish left in it. They came flipping out onto the deck just as John came running back with his little fish bowl.

"What's that?" asked a fisherman.

"A fish bowl," Ole answered, climbing up on to the boat. "Don't you know a fish bowl when you see one? Stand back, fellows! I told John he could have his pick. Well, sonny, which will it be? Go ahead, pick out any one you want for your bowl."

"Woof!" Pogo barked at the big fish by John's feet. It was as big as Pogo.

John looked all over the deck. "Aren't there going to be any more?" he asked.

"Not this time. They're all on board." Ole waved his hand. "Look them over. Which one will you have?"

John looked at all of the fish carefully.

"Why there isn't even one little one!" John said, then he began to laugh. He looked at his little bowl and the big fish and laughed some more. Uncle Edward laughed. Ole and Bill laughed and all the rest of the fishermen laughed too. It was funny just to think of putting such a big fish in such a little bowl.

Uncle Edward held up the end of the net and showed John the big openings between the strings. "You see," he laughed, "all the little fish swim right out."

"Of course!" said John, "I never thought of that."

"Anyway, even little fish from the ocean would not be happy in your bowl. They have to stay in the salt water," Uncle Edward said. "But never you mind. I know where you can find just the right little fish for your bowl. Hey, Bill?"

"Yes, sir! He's been waiting for you a long time. Only yesterday he said to me, 'When is John coming? I do need a new house.' And I said, 'Pretty soon now.'" Bill winked at John. "You come over to my yard when we go ashore."

Mother and Father were on Uncle Edward's porch when the *Alice B.* came home again.

"We missed you," said Father.

John kissed Mother and whispered something in her ear.

Mother smiled and nodded. "We must take the next ferry, so don't be gone too long."

"We won't," promised Bill. He took John's hand and led him behind the little house next door to a pool among some rocks.

Mother and Daddy could see the ferry coming across the water. "Goodbye!" they called to Uncle Edward. "We had such a nice time on the beach!"

Father was putting the big suitcases in the car. "Hurry, John!" he called.

"Wait!" called John. "I'm here with Bill. I have to get something!"

Soon he came walking slowly with something held carefully in his hands.

"What is that?" asked Father.

Mother said, "He has his wish."

"A pretty little golden fish!" said John.

"Woof! Woof! Woof!" said Pogo.

MOST HOLY TRINITY SCHOOL
3946 Wooddale Avenue
St. Louis Park, Minn. 55416

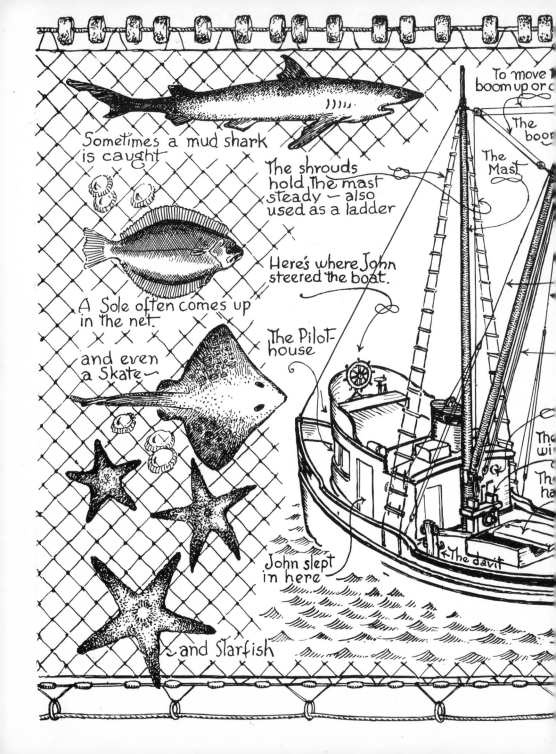

Sometimes a mud shark is caught

The shrouds hold the mast steady — also used as a ladder

To move the boom up or down

The boom

The Mast

Here's where John steered the boat.

A Sole often comes up in the net.

The Pilot-house

and even a Skate —

The winch

The hatch

John slept in here

← The davit

_ and Starfish

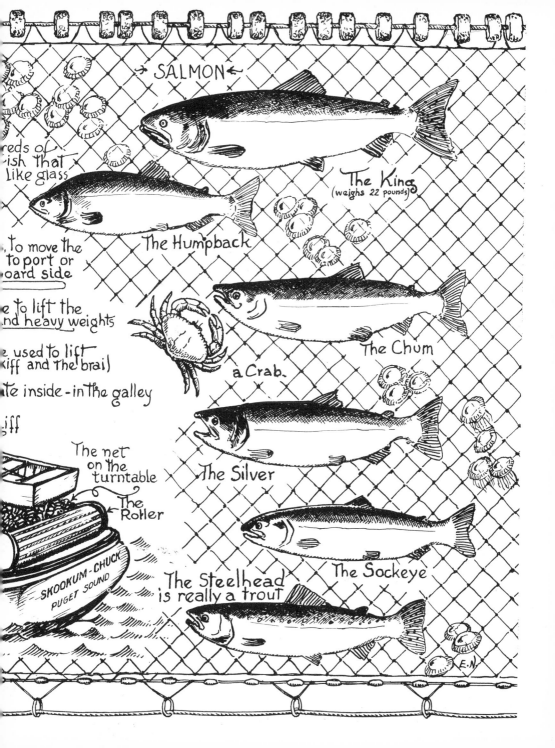

SALMON

The King
(weighs 22 pounds)

The Humpback

reds of
ish that
Like glass

to move the
to port or
oard side

e to lift the
nd heavy weights

e used to lift
kiff and the brail

te inside - in the galley

iff

a Crab.

The Chum

The net
on the
turntable

The
Rotler

SKOOKUM-CHUCK
PUGET SOUND

The Silver

The Steelhead
is really a trout

The Sockeye

E·N